# Contents

First published in 2007
© Demos
Some rights reserved – see copyright licence for details

Series edited by Charles Leadbeater and James Wilsdon

ISBN 1 84180 174 7
Copy edited by Julie Pickard, London
Design by Browns (www.brownsdesign.com)
Printed by The Good News Press

For further information and subscription details please contact:
Demos, Magdalen House, 136 Tooley Street, London, SE1 2TU
telephone: 0845 458 5949 email: hello@demos.co.uk
web: www.demos.co.uk

'Chinese R&D has been rising by 20 per cent a year over the past five years. South Korean R&D has increased tenfold since 1971. Indian R&D is even more astonishing – it has trebled in a decade. Indian engineers are flooding into the world's markets – 350,000 a year, forecast to reach 1.4 million a year by 2015.'

Tony Blair MP, Prime Minister, November 2006

India
Chapter 2
P17

'In 20 years global science will be driven by Indian scientists. There are new interfaces in science, with new rules, where new countries can contribute on an equal footing.'

Dr Vijay Raghavan, director, National Centre for Biological Sciences Bangalore, January 2006

China
Chapter 1
P03

'By the end of 2020... China will achieve more science and technological breakthroughs of great world influence, qualifying it to join the ranks of the world's most innovative countries.'

President Hu Jintao, January 2006

# 1 Look east

On the outskirts of Shanghai, 1000 researchers are working in a state of the art Intel research facility that was built from scratch in just five months. By 2012 there could be 10,000 spread over two sites. In Beijing, engineers at Ericsson's research centre are developing routers for mobile phone systems at a third of the cost of those in Europe. On the edge of New Delhi, among the call centres and new shopping malls, Ranbaxy, the Indian drug company, has opened an R&D centre with 2000 scientists, modelled on a Bristol-Myers Squibb facility in the US. In Daejon in South Korea, geneticists equipped with the latest gene-sequencing machines are generating world-class stomach cancer research after just three years. The knowledge parks and high-tech zones springing up across Asia are demolishing the barriers to entry into scientific innovation.

Flowing through the airports that serve Asia's innovation hotspots are the people who make this shiny hardware work: research scientists, corporate innovation managers and serial entrepreneurs, flooding back mainly from the US and carrying with them western management methods, money, contacts and ambition. They are attracted by a potent cocktail: fast-growing markets; plentiful state funding for research; and middle-class lifestyles in increasingly cosmopolitan cities that they can call home.

The reverse migration of these nomad innovators heralds a new phase of globalisation, one in which ideas and innovation will flow from many more sources. In the last 30 years, global supply chains have transformed how we make products. Our pensions, savings and bank accounts now depend on seamlessly connected global markets. Something similar is about to happen to the way we develop and apply ideas. Innovation will emerge from global networks that link research, testing, development and application.

We used to expect new ideas to come from the universities and research laboratories of major companies in the US and Europe. Technology flowed from this innovative core to the technologically dependent periphery. No more. The core and periphery are being scrambled up. Places that were on the margins of innovation ten years ago – Bangalore and Pune in India, Daejon in Korea, Shanghai and Shenzhen in China – are now essential stopping-off points in the continuous flow of people, ideas and technologies around the world.

The rise of China, India and South Korea will remake the innovation landscape. US and European pre-eminence in science-based innovation cannot be taken for granted. The centre of gravity for innovation is starting to shift from west to east. This report explains what is happening and how the UK should respond.

China
Chapter 2
P14

China's share of the world's science publications –
up from 2 per cent to 6.5 per cent in under ten years

## Percentage of world share of scientific publications

|      | China | France | Germany | Japan | Korea | UK   | US    | EU-15 |
|------|-------|--------|---------|-------|-------|------|-------|-------|
| 1995 | 2.05  | 6.09   | 7.62    | 8.65  | 0.79  | 8.88 | 33.54 | 34.36 |
| 1998 | 2.90  | 6.48   | 8.82    | 9.42  | 1.41  | 9.08 | 31.63 | 36.85 |
| 2001 | 4.30  | 6.33   | 8.68    | 9.52  | 2.01  | 8.90 | 31.01 | 36.55 |
| 2004 | 6.52  | 5.84   | 8.14    | 8.84  | 2.70  | 8.33 | 30.48 | 35.18 |

Source: Adapted from P Zhou and L Leydesdorff, 'The emergence of China as a leading nation
in science' *Research Policy* 35, no 1 (Feb 2006).

Korea
Chapter 2
P15

## Growth in US patents* 1992–2005

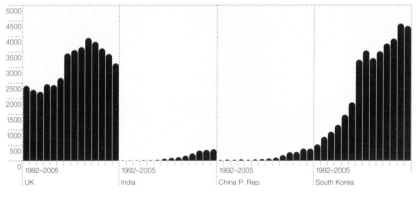

*Patents issued by the US Patent and Trademark Office
Source: US Patent and Trademark Office, see www.uspto.gov/go/taf/cst_utl.htm

India
Chapter 2
P09

India produces 2.5 million graduates in information technology, engineering
and life sciences each year.

# 2 What is at stake?

The rise of innovation from China, India and Korea is feeding a climate of anxiety in Europe and the US that could lead to defensive responses. A combination of knowledge jobs being offshored and a heightened techno-nationalism in Asia could provoke a similar response in the West.

Britain must avoid making two big mistakes. First, it must wake up to what is unfolding in China and India, and not respond with too little too late. Second, it must work to prevent a global retreat into techno-nationalism, and instead evangelise for a cosmopolitan approach to innovation.

The rise of Asia will inevitably challenge our position in knowledge-based industries. More knowledge jobs will go offshore. Research and development will become more international. In the long run, China, India and Korea will start to earn more from exploiting their own intellectual property, and our share of income from intellectual property may decline.

However, it would be extremely short-sighted to view these developments purely as a competitive threat.

Britain can prosper from global innovation networks, as it has from the internationalisation of financial services, but only if we choose not to isolate ourselves from global flows of knowledge. We need to act decisively to make ourselves central to global innovation networks, based on a longer-term view of what is at stake both for Britain and the rest of the world.

Innovation in Asia may accelerate development and raise incomes, creating a larger market for British services. The resources India and China are devoting to innovation are large, but still feeble when set against the challenges of the poverty they face. In India, 390 million people live on less than US$1 a day, often without clean water and electricity. Some of China's poorest regions have a standard of living on a par with the poorer parts of Africa. These countries need innovation to deliver tangible social improvements. The more successful they are, the more opportunities there will be for Britain to trade with them.

Innovators in Britain may also be more productive if they can collaborate with Asian partners with complementary skills, for example in the application and development of technology. Our hubs of scientific innovation, in London, Cambridge, Oxford and Manchester, should attract inflows of talent from around the world, just as the City of London has.

If more researchers are doing more science, with ever more powerful computers, this increases the likelihood of meeting the global scientific challenges we face: from low-carbon innovation to vaccines against pandemics. More brains, working on more ideas, in more places around the world, are good news for innovation. Out of that may come new fields of science, such as synthetic biology, and new methods that transform how science is done.

India
Chapter 2
P18

'There is no such thing as an innovation system in India. An innovation system means a chain linking all the way from idea to customer service... There is no clear path in India – sure we have ideas, but then what do we do with them? There is a big gap in terms of translational research. At every part of the chain there is a hurdle. We need a proper innovation system!'

Professor Jayesh Bellare, Department of Chemical Engineering, IIT Bombay

China
Chapter 1
P04

Since 1999, China's spending on research and development (R&D) has increased by more than 20 per cent each year. In 2005, it reached 1.3 per cent of gross domestic product (GDP), up from 0.7 per cent in 1998. In December 2006, the Organisation for Economic Co-operation and Development (OECD) surprised policy-makers by announcing that China had moved ahead of Japan for the first time, to become the world's second highest R&D investor after the US. Spending by central government in 2006 reached 71.6 billion RMB, or £4.7 billion, compared with £3.2 billion by the UK government.

Korea
Chapter 1
P06

South Korean gross expenditure on R&D was almost 3 per cent of GDP in 2005, about 75 per cent of it from private industry. Public funding for R&D in 2006 was US$8.65 billion, a 15 per cent increase over 2005. Korea is ranked fifteenth in the world in terms of scientific publications. Korea has the highest annual growth in patent families – more than 20 per cent – and the highest growth in US patents from 1986 to 2003. The Korean government will increase the R&D labour force from 180,000 to 250,000 by 2007.

# 3 There is no Asian innovation model

China's political elite ended the twentieth century much as it started: obsessed by the country's technological standing in the world. Defeat by the Japanese in 1906 underlined how far China's technology had fallen behind. By the 1970s, it was in even worse shape, as the Cultural Revolution ravaged the scientific research base.

But a country whose leaders mostly trained as engineers is now engaged in the biggest mobilisation of scientific resources since John F Kennedy launched the race to put a man on the moon. Massive increases in government R&D spending, rising multinational investment in innovation and flows of researchers, entrepreneurs and managers returning from Europe and the US are fuelling China's ambitions to become a science superpower, less reliant on foreign technology thanks to a new generation of home-grown hi-tech companies. China's hopes are that its most innovative regions will soon be where South Korea is now.

South Korea emerged in 1960 from a ruinous civil war, its economy on its knees, with virtually no natural resources, low levels of literacy, just 800 graduates and GDP per capita on a par with some African states. With US support, the state-orchestrated rapid industrial development working hand in glove with a group of large, family-owned companies. That provided the base for Korea's ambitions to become a knowledge-driven economy, with R&D set to reach 3 per cent of GDP by 2010. Korea plans to be a world leader in biotech and nanotechnology, through doubling investment in R&D to expand the scientific research workforce from 180,000 to 250,000. Korea's well-educated population, connected by pervasive broadband and mobile phone penetration, could unleash a wave of mass innovation in media and services.

India is a different story altogether. China is a one-party state, India an imperfect but vibrant democracy. In Korea the state orchestrated development; in India the state is chaotic at best, and at worst a drag on innovation. In Korea, work is defined by the phrase 'hurry, hurry'; India is more languid. China is seeking to become a source of 'independent innovation'. India has already turned away from that goal. Political independence from Britain in 1947 ushered in a concerted attempt to build a self-reliant Indian science and innovation system. But since India opened its economy to international investment and trade in 1991, it has positioned itself as an *interdependent* innovator, serving multinational companies and creating technologies for global markets.

India's innovative energy comes from its people: 2.5 million graduates a year, 350,000 of them engineers. By 2015 India could be producing 1.4 million graduate engineers a year. At the heart of this is a group of global Indians, who many hope will lead the country's transformation. India does not have an innovation system but an innovation class: the global, non-resident Indians, who are embedded in social and business networks that connect India to Silicon Valley and beyond.

There is no Asian innovation model; there are several.

India
Chapter 2
P15

A study by Sir David King, the UK's chief scientific adviser, published in *Nature* in 2004, assessed national research performance based on a range of criteria, including share of the top 1 per cent of highly cited publications. India came twenty-second, with a total of 77,201 publications between 1997 and 2001, of which 205 were in the top 1 per cent of highly cited publications. This compares with 375 in the top 1 per cent for China and 4381 for the UK. India was ranked at the very bottom of King's sample when pitting citation achievements against national wealth measured by GDP.

But as Dr Mashelkar has pointed out: 'Nothing looks big when you divide by a billion!' Mashelkar has turned King's paper on its head by examining the relationship between citations and GDP per capita, by which reckoning India belongs at the very top of the table. King's analysis shows a country punching well below its potential weight, yet that of Mashelkar tells us that India's science is hugely successful for a country where most people are poor.

Korea
Chapter 2
P14

While Korean scientists published 81,057 papers between 2000 and 2004, their work is not frequently cited by other scientists. Despite being fifteenth in the world in terms of papers published, in 2005 Korea could not claim a position in the top 20 countries for citations.

China
Chapter 1
P07

So much of China's growth and development has relied on imported technologies that only 0.03 per cent of Chinese firms own the intellectual property rights of the core technologies they use. This acts as a serious constraint on profitability. Universities and research institutes are becoming more productive, but Chinese enterprises still lag behind in terms of R&D intensity and patenting, spending on average only 0.56 per cent of turnover on R&D expenditure. Even in large firms this rises to just 0.71 per cent.

# 4  In the hall of mirrors

Judging what kind of innovation these three different countries could produce is complicated. It is easy to both underestimate and overestimate what they are capable of. It is like being in a fairground hall of mirrors: the same statistics can simultaneously look very large or very small depending on your vantage point. In India these problems are further compounded because reliable information is sometimes not available.

Four problems bedevil attempts to make reliable judgements about the strength of these innovation systems.

### Quantity does not mean quality
India has a huge pool of young graduates but perhaps only 10 per cent of them have an education of international quality. Korea produces scientific papers in prodigious quantity but most tend not to be heavily cited by other scientists, which suggests that their quality and originality is not high.

### Choose the right yardstick
China and India's aggregate output of science and scientists is growing fast. Yet, set against the size of their population, science is underdeveloped: India produces large numbers of engineers in global terms, but still only 5 per cent of its population goes to university.

### Inputs do not equate to outputs
Innovation measures focus on the resources being pumped into science and research. How productively these resources are used also matters. Here the picture is more mixed. In China, for example, it is common for policy-makers to point out that world-class hardware and infrastructure for innovation does not equate to world-class culture and software for innovation.

### It is still early days
Korea seemed to be leading the world in stem cell research until the results of now disgraced researcher Dr Hwang, then Korea's supreme scientist, were exposed as fraudulent. Similar 'science bubbles' may inflate in China where resources are pouring into a research system which insiders say is rife with plagiarism. China faces larger uncertainties over whether economic growth can be maintained, the prospects for political reform, and whether top-down planning will stifle innovation even as it funds it. In India the inequalities associated with globalisation have provoked a cultural and political backlash that has forced politicians to refocus on the needs of the rural poor. Only ten years ago India was still seen by many as a case for aid; now equally erroneously it is sometimes assumed that India is becoming a vast software park.

Innovation is not linear. It does not roll off a production line, with researchers, equipment and resources going in at one end and papers, patents and applications flowing out at the other. China, India and South Korea will be more significant sources of innovation in future. What kinds of innovation they produce remains to be seen.

| 1 | Re-emergence |
|---|---|
| 2 | The state's role in science |
| 3 | Cultural tensions |
| 4 | Relationship with the outside |

Korea
Chapter 3
P22

'The values of openness, disinterestedness, and cooperation will come to be seen as equally important as market principles and global standards... We don't know what the state of the university will be in three or five years. It's not stable.'

Un-Chan Chung, former president of Seoul National University

India
Chapter 1
P05

For centuries, India was the world's largest economy, producing a third of global GDP. Evidence of advanced technological culture comes from archaeology as well as scripture. The Harappans in 2500BC had a sewage system at their city of Mohenjo-Daro and carefully laid out streets, indicating advanced notions of geometry. Ayurveda, the science of longevity, which still plays a significant role in Indian medicine, dates back to 800BC. India developed the mathematical concept of zero in about AD600, as well as the decimal system. Even Pythagoras, in the sixth century BC, is said to have learnt his basic geometry from the Sulva Sutras. By 200BC, Indian scientists were the first in the world to be smelting iron with carbon to make steel.

China
Chapter 1
P11

In a recent essay, Joshua Cooper Ramo speaks of the difficulty of finding a national framework 'capable of containing both the lively energy of Shanghai and the grinding poverty of Gansu, both the joy of expanding liberty and the too-frequent chill of restricted freedom, both the warm hearts of the Chinese people and their deep fear of social instability and foreign influence'.

# 5 Common themes

Despite their significant differences, innovation in China, India and South Korea will share certain themes.

These are not emerging science powers but re-emerging. In all these countries science has an ancient history. In Europe, we associate science with modernity. In these societies, science is also associated with antiquity. The combination of modern scientific techniques with ancient and alternative forms of knowledge may yet bear fruit in areas such as health care.

All are emerging, hesitantly, from economies that were heavily regulated by the state. In Korea the state organised industrial development by carving up markets for favoured chaebol. The 1997 financial crisis led to IMF-enforced reforms, which some critics allege are now running out of steam. In India, innovation was kick-started by the 1991 economic reforms, but the piecemeal dismantling of the so-called 'license Raj' still has a long way to go. In China, the state is attempting simultaneously to control and deregulate the economy, for example through the creation of new zones for economic reform in Pudong and Binhai. How far and fast these reforms go will determine to what extent innovation is driven by the market or the state.

Reforms to promote innovation are triggering cultural and social tensions, as reformers in favour of more open, cosmopolitan and market-based approaches find themselves pitted against defenders of more inward-looking, state-sponsored solutions. As Ze Zhang, the vice president of Beijing University of Technology and former general secretary of the Chinese Association for Science and Technology, put it: 'Everyone [talks] constantly of innovation. But I think we are only just beginning to understand what this word really means. It's like gears grinding against one another. There's a lot of tension between the push for innovation and the capacity of the political system to deliver it.' The pursuit of innovation is triggering cultural clashes that will claim more casualties like Robert Laughlin, the US Nobel prize-winning physicist who was brought in to turn around KAIST, Korea's leading research institute. Laughlin was ousted after staff mutinied against his reform plans.

Science and innovation also reveals these countries' intense and sometimes insecure relationships with outsiders. All three countries are hungry for international recognition as equals of the developed economies. In South Korea and China, science and technology are projections of national power and virility. The disgraced Dr Hwang claimed to be 'planting the Korean flag in the heart of western science'.

Yet the reality is that science and innovation will require these countries to be more open to global flows of ideas and people. Modern Indian science, for example, is a complex mix of institutions inherited from the British Raj, state-sponsored programmes started after Independence and companies created out of more recent connections with the US and Silicon Valley. Growing involvement with science will make these societies more cosmopolitan even as they aim to develop science for nationalistic goals.

India
Chapter 6
P40

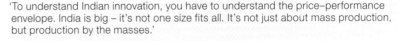

'To understand Indian innovation, you have to understand the price–performance envelope. India is big – it's not one size fits all. It's not just about mass production, but production by the masses.'

Dr RA Mashelkar, director general, CSIR

Korea
Chapter 5
P32

Wan-Joo Kim, founder of C-TRI, a small pharmaceutical company and one of the first researchers who returned from the US to work at the Korea Institute of Science and Technology, described the change: 'Before 1997, we were only imitating. Now it is totally different.'

China
Chapter 5
P42

Ian Harvey, chairman of the Intellectual Property Institute, points out that there are three components to an effective IP regime: the underpinning law, the cost and quality of the patent 'right' acquired, and the effectiveness and cost of enforcing that right. Against each of these criteria, China now performs well: following a series of measures, its legal infrastructure 'is among the best in the world'; IP 'rights' are generally of good quality and cost around 10 per cent of their equivalents in most G8 countries; and enforcement through the courts is also cheap and takes little more than a year, compared with five to seven years in the US.

# 6 Eight forces in the new geography of science

## 1 The momentum of the market

Innovation will be pulled by the market. Western firms will do more R&D closer to their growing pool of Asian consumers. Growing markets will also support a new generation of high-tech Asian companies.

Under a system of state planning, innovation to expand market share was pointless. But India and China now have a combined population of 2.3 billion and are creating an urban middle class on a vast scale, which will demand more sophisticated, branded consumer goods.

China already has 90 cities with more than one million inhabitants and is expected to create 60 more in the next 20 years. ABB, the engineering group, has shifted more of its R&D to Beijing because China is the world's fastest-growing electricity market with a new coal-fired power station built every four days. Ericsson, Nokia and Vodafone are doing more R&D in China because it is adding 60 million mobile phone subscribers a year: the size of the entire UK market. The growing market for air travel is one factor behind Airbus's decision to locate more production and development in China. Even Bill Gates, a long time critic of China's weak enforcement of copyright law, now believes intellectual property will be protected.

India, with 17 per cent of the world's population but only 2.5 per cent of global GDP, is enjoying economic growth of about 8 per cent. Goldman Sachs recently predicted India could grow faster than China over the long run thanks to its young and growing population. Three-quarters of the Indian population is under the age of 25. Most remain poor: about 80 per cent live on less than US$2 a day. Reaching markets of hundreds of millions of poor consumers will require radical, low-cost innovations, such as the $100 computer, which could eventually disrupt core developed markets.

Korea, one of the most educated and connected societies in the world, shows how advanced consumer demand can propel innovation. Korea has the highest rates of broadband and mobile phone penetration in the OECD. By 2008, high-speed mobile internet access should be pervasive. The government hopes tech-savvy and demanding consumers will rapidly take up new technologies and services – like mobile phone health monitors – that will provide Korean technology companies with a head start in world markets.

Growing markets will also provide political leverage. China will try to make access to Chinese markets dependent on technical standards that favour domestic champions, and reduce reliance on standards set by consortia of foreign companies.

Korea
Chapter 1
P07

Korean companies, universities and state think tanks together spent 24.15 trillion won (US$25.03 billion) on R&D in 2005. The budget for key 'new growth' technologies will rise from 28.5 per cent of the total in 2004 to 50 per cent by 2012. The Ministry of Information and Communications (MIC) 'Ubiquitous Korea' or 'U-Korea' IT839 Strategy is designed to help Korea realise a digital welfare state, at a cost to government and private industry of US$70 billion by 2010. The Korea Bio-Vision 2010 aims to push Korea's biotech ranking from thirteenth in the world in 2003 to seventh by 2010, and to be among the top three countries in biotech by 2015. Government plans are for Korea to have ten cutting-edge nanotechnologies and 12,600 nanotechnology experts by 2010.

China
Chapter 1
P05

In January 2006, China's Science and Technology Congress met for three days to approve a new Medium to Long-Term Science and Technology Development Plan. This identifies priorities for the next 15 years and confirms the aim of boosting investment to 2 per cent of GDP by 2010 and 2.5 per cent by 2020. The plan says that advances in science and technology should eventually account for 60 per cent of economic growth, and that China should aim to be among the top five countries worldwide in terms of patents and scientific citations. In his keynote speech to the Congress on 9 January 2006, President Hu Jintao called on China to become an 'innovation-oriented society'.

## 2 State support

Governments are using the proceeds from sustained economic growth to invest more in innovation through dedicated research programmes, new institutions of science and more university research. However, policy-makers in all three countries want to reform their innovation systems to make them more productive, less disjointed and more internationally connected.

China's R&D spending has been growing at close to 20 per cent a year since 1999, with plans for it to rise to 2.5 per cent of GDP by 2020. In Korea, R&D spending has risen from just 0.39 per cent in 1970 to close to 3 per cent today. Although the private sector accounts for the lion's share – 75 per cent – public R&D will account for 7 per cent of government expenditure in 2007.

India does not conform to the Asian tiger model of state-driven development. Yet even the Indian state may be acquiring some stripes. About 80 per cent of Indian R&D is publicly funded. In October 2006 Prime Minister Manmohan Singh announced plans to raise R&D from 0.8 per cent of GDP to 2 per cent by 2012. In 2005, R&D spending rose by 24 per cent to about $4.5 billion.

Indian modernisers are trying to shift research spending into more productive areas. The government runs 400 laboratories of variable quality. RA Mashelkar, until late 2006 the head of the Council for Scientific and Industrial Research, the government science and innovation agency, developed plans for a raft of new institutions, including a National Science and Engineering Foundation for fundamental research, and two new Indian Institutes of Scientific Education and Research.

Ambitious state investment brings risks as well as resources. Critics of the Chinese research system argue that much of the increased investment in science will be wasted through poorly run programmes, with weak peer review and governance. In Korea, critics of Dr Hwang, the disgraced stem cell scientist, argue that he faked his findings because he was under government pressure to deliver eye-catching results. Innovation cannot be delivered to a plan.

High levels of state investment in research in China and Korea comes with a price: the expectation of rapid results that can be translated quickly into commercial applications. That will make life uncomfortable for many scientists and could lead to more scandals.

India
Chapter 5
P33

Chosen as one of Red Herring's top 100 Innovative Asian companies in 2005, Ittiam, short for 'I think therefore I am', designs software for portable devices like digital cameras and MP3 players. CEO Srini Rajan had a long career with Texas Instruments, culminating in becoming managing director for its Indian subsidiary in 1995. He set up Ittiam with six Texas Instruments colleagues in 2001: 'We wanted to do something that was beyond entrepreneurship. We thought that India needed to create giants of its own. That it needed companies with drive and passion, even nationalism.'

Only one in every 500 applicants for a job at Ittiam makes the cut. The company presentation to new recruits focuses on its Indian roots, Rajan explained: 'I make a lot out of the fact that we are Indian and we are going places.' Investors, on the other hand, see a presentation that focuses only on Ittiam's position as a global competitor.

Korea
Chapter 2
P13

Unlike in China and India, Korea's own multinationals account for 75 per cent of the gross expenditure on R&D, and just 0.5 per cent of total R&D investment came from foreign sources in 2004.

China
Chapter 5
P40

'At first, the research we were doing was related to market access. But to be honest, we've found it even more cost effective to do R&D here than I thought was possible. The speed with which we can develop prototypes is key. The turnaround is so fast, so that even if the quality is a little lower, we get them so quickly that we can have many more attempts at getting them right. We get more shots at the same problem for a lower cost.'

Ralph Lofdahl, general manager, Radio Network R&D Center, Beijing

## 3 Multinational innovation

Famous corporate names are setting up research facilities in knowledge parks all over India and China. From Intel and Microsoft, to Siemens and Vodafone, to Unilever and Merck, multinational companies are attracted by growing markets and the pool of cheap but highly skilled labour emerging from elite universities.

Research and development was traditionally a headquarters function, done close to home. But in the last five years, advances in computing and communications, combined with experience of offshoring other activities, has made large companies far more adept at innovating through global networks. As one Intel executive in Shanghai put it:

*Decisions about where to locate manufacturing are relatively easy. It's now a science, with established methodologies. But locating R&D is more of an art. For Intel, our top factors are: 1) people; 2) people; 3) people; 4) customers; 5) government.*

In China, there were about 20 multinational R&D centres in 1997; by 2006, official figures put the total at 750. India hosts about 150 centres, more than 100 of them opened since 2002. Korea wants to become a hub for R&D in north-east Asia, attracting multinational companies to free economic zones like Incheon. But it is starting from a very low base: only 0.4 per cent of Korean R&D is done by foreign companies.

These research centres are no longer just adapting western products for local markets. Almost without exception the 80 international R&D managers we spoke to said they were researching technologies to create products with global potential. Research centres like Microsoft's in Beijing or Adobe's near New Delhi are global centres of excellence.

In China, R&D managers acknowledged it could take time to foster creativity among staff who were mainly educated through rote learning. However, they argued that western-style management combined with a Chinese collective work ethic was a potent combination.

Companies like Intel and GE are endorsing the quality of Indian and Chinese research and the improving environment for intellectual property protection. These centres bring critical skills in innovation management that are in short supply locally.

Yet multinational research centres may be a mixed blessing. They attract the brightest and best researchers away from the public sector and indigenous companies. There seems to be little mobility between multinational centres and local companies in either India or China. Entrepreneurial spin-outs from multinationals are still rare.

Multinational research centres will benefit India and China only if they increasingly interact with local economies through spin-offs, labour mobility and partnerships with smaller companies and universities. Until then, as Professor Belaram, director of the Indian Institute of Science in Bengalooru, says: 'These companies are only geographically located here. They contribute little to the science base here. In fact as the R&D centres grow the interaction with science diminishes.'

India
Chapter 2
P14

The Indian Institutes of Technology have played a starring role in India's apparent début on the global stage of science and technology. They are at the top of an enormous heap of engineering graduates, but one that suffers drastic variations in quality. They may seem to represent the future of Indian science education in the making, but they have special status outside the inadequate university infrastructure. Only a tiny 1 per cent of applicants achieve a place in an IIT, and there are only seven of these institutes for a country of 1.1 billion people. The quality of the graduates produced may be world-beating, but they do relatively little research, in a national system where higher education and research remain highly separated undertakings. A huge percentage of IITians go abroad after their studies even today, and many would estimate that they have contributed more to the innovation systems of other countries than to the knowledge base of India. The challenge remains whether India can create a broader-based infrastructure for excellent technological education.

China
Chapter 3
P30

Universities are improving in quality. Curricula have improved, new courses have been introduced, and programmes are less ideological than in the past. There are more visiting foreign professors, exchange programmes and joint centres linked with overseas universities. China is investing in a core group of elite universities such as Tsinghua, Beijing, Fudan and Nanjing universities, which it wants to be world-class institutions. This policy is already paying off: both Beijing and Tsinghua are now in the world's top 100 universities, and four or five others are rising up fast. As a result, more students are willing to stay in China for postgraduate study than in the past.

## 4 People and skills

India and China are creating large pools of talent, skilled in disciplines such as physics and chemistry that are increasingly falling out of fashion in the UK and the US. Between them South China, India and Korea have about 2500 universities. The UK has 120.

India's domestic talent pool comprises 14 million recent graduates, 1.5 times the number in China and twice the US. India produces 2.5 million new graduates a year in IT, engineering and life sciences, with 650,000 postgraduates and between 4000 and 6000 PhDs. The pinnacle of the India system is the seven Indian Institutes of Technology. Six Chinese universities are already in the *Times Higher Education Supplement*'s worldwide top 200 and the government is investing heavily in a core group of about 100 to raise them to international standards.

China enrolled 4.74 million undergraduates in 2004, up from one million a decade before, and produced 23,500 PhDs in 2005, 70 per cent of them in science and engineering. China has 1731 colleges and universities with more being created the whole time. About 820,000 postgraduates a year emerge from 769 graduate and research centres. The main university district of Beijing is home to 50 universities. This area alone produces more science and engineering graduates than most of Europe.

Korea prospered after its civil war only through heavy public and private investment in education. By 2006, about 95 per cent of Korean 25–34-year-olds had at least a secondary school leaving certificate and 80 per cent of young Koreans study at university. In 1970, Korea's 142 higher education institutions enrolled 201,000 students. In 2004, 411 institutions enrolled 3.5 million, about 40 per cent of them in science and engineering.

Yet despite leading the world in secondary education, Korean universities lag behind. Only one Korean institution – KAIST – made it into the *Times* top 200.

India is in a similar position. RA Mashelkar, the head of India's Council for Scientific and Industrial Research, estimates that only 10 per cent of India's 229 universities do world-class research. Even the most prestigious institutions find it difficult to recruit staff owing to competition from multinational companies; the Indian Institute of Technology in New Delhi, for example, is short of about 100 faculty.

Far from being plentiful, some scientific skills are in short supply. Dr Bhattacharya, director of the Tata Institute for Fundamental Research in Mumbai, complained: 'The biggest bottleneck in Indian science is not money – it's a lack of people and a lack of ideas. The human resource crunch is the single biggest difficulty that India faces.'

In India and China, a lot rests on whether bringing back skilled people from the US and Europe can solve the problem.

India
Chapter 3
P22

'The old pattern of one-way flows of technology and capital from the core to the periphery is being replaced by a far more complex and decentralised two-way flow of skill, capital and technology between differently specialised regional economies.'

AnnaLee Saxenian, author of *The New Argonauts*

'Of all India's natural assets, it is the non-resident Indian base that has a far greater value than anything else.'

Ramalingu Raju, CEO, Satyam Computers

China
Chapter 3
P29

'If the US is playing sport, we cheer the US. If China is playing, we cheer China. And if the US is playing China, we cheer China. But no-one gets rid of their green card or their US passport. We may have come home but we will always keep our options open.'

Jin Kewen, Shanghai-based returnee

## 5 The talent Gulf Stream

They are coming home to roost. Since the 1970s, many of the brightest Indian and Chinese students, despairing of the limited opportunities on offer at home, went abroad to work and study, mainly in the US. Between 1978 and 2006 about 700,000 Chinese students left to study abroad.

In the last decade, these people flows have started to go both ways. About 170,000 Chinese students have returned from abroad. One estimate is that 30,000 Indian software programmers have returned home from the US. Brain drain has turned to brain gain as scientists bring back research techniques and know-how to set up new publicly funded labs, entrepreneurs bring money and ambition to set up new business ventures, and multinational managers help navigate their companies into knowledge parks in Bengalooru and Shanghai.

These returnees could be more critical to innovation than either large companies or state R&D programmes. Many of them keep a foot in both camps. In China we met scientists and entrepreneurs who commuted to Los Angeles or Washington DC to see their spouses and children. Nor do they necessarily fully integrate back home. Li Gong, managing director of Microsoft's Windows Live in Beijing, speaks for many Chinese returnees when he says they are 'kept outside the centre, in the import zone'. Worse, some face hostility from colleagues who have never been abroad or whose status may be threatened by returnees.

Returnees will energise, challenge and orchestrate innovation in India and China. Whether this circulation of talent is a permanent feature, however, depends on a number of factors. Younger generations in China and India seem to want to work abroad for only four or five years before returning, whereas their parents' generation worked abroad for 15 or 20. If economic opportunities at home continue to grow, more will be drawn back, especially if the cultural climate for foreigners working in the US continues to remain clouded as it has been since 9/11. Overt government policies – such as China's '100 Talents' programme and the Indian government's creation of a new form of dual-citizenship status – can also help to bring people back.

China in particular may have seen only the first wave of returnees. About 80 per cent of those who left in the 1980s have not returned. These include some of the most successful scientists and entrepreneurs. They could have a huge impact on China, but they seem unlikely to return in droves without further political reform. China's national ambitions in science and technology could rest on creating conditions that can attract the most cosmopolitan group of knowledge workers in the world.

Korea
Chapter 5
P34

'Since 2001, the reform drive has ground to a halt. Some observers say it has gone into reverse, enabling Korea's chaebol conglomerates to reassert their stranglehold, stitching up domestic markets and stifling the emergence of new businesses.'

Guy de Jonquieres, Asia business commentator, *Financial Times*

China
Chapter 5
P41

China's largest high-tech firms, such as Huawei and Lenovo (which in December 2004 acquired IBM's PC division), do appear to be prioritising research and development. Huawei now has R&D centres in Bengalooru, Dallas, San Diego, Amsterdam, Stockholm and Moscow, as well as 10,000 research staff in China... Other companies investing significantly in R&D include Sina and Sohu, China's largest web portals; Shanda, the online gaming provider; and Huaqi, which makes MP3 players under its Aigo brand and has 200 of its 1500 staff in R&D. Yet these companies remain the exception in a country where business R&D is still relatively underdeveloped.

India
Chapter 5
P36

The venture capital industry in India is still at an early stage, despite huge increases in the numbers and size of funds over the past five years. Estimates suggest that total private equity investments in India have soared to $5.4 billion in only the first nine months of 2006. This compares with a total of $2.2 billion in total last year... American private equity firms are leading the pack; many have permanent offices in India: the largest investment was the $900 million buyout of Flextronics software by an American firm.

## 6 Homegrown enterprise

Increased investment in science and technology will feed long-term growth only if it connects with a wave of entrepreneurship from start-ups and larger, more established businesses. Multinational companies are conspicuous in Asia's knowledge parks. Home-grown innovation is harder to find.

In India, for example, 86 per cent of companies do no R&D. In colonial times they imported technology. Post-independence they operated in managed markets. Even the poster boys of corporate India, the giant software services companies, prosper by servicing western companies rather than creating their own products: Infosys spends less than 1 per cent of its sales on R&D. Though venture capital funds are expanding, entrepreneurs face daunting risks. Even promising start-ups from prestigious research institutions complain it is difficult to raise funding.

There are bright spots: in the next ten years, India will produce new models of indigenous innovation from the pharmaceutical sector, where R&D spending rose by 300 per cent in the last five years. This may lead in turn to change in other sectors.

China produces three out of every four photocopiers in the world and half of its DVDs. High-tech exports are growing at 22 per cent a year. Yet just 0.03 per cent of Chinese firms own the intellectual property on the core technology in their products, in part because Chinese companies spend just 0.56 per cent of sales on R&D. Smaller companies account for 65 per cent of Chinese patents and 80 per cent of new products, according to the Ministry of Science and Technology. But venture capitalists say there are still few signs of a Silicon Valley style start-up culture.

China's leadership sees it as a matter of national prestige to create home-grown technology champions. About 95 per cent of cars on Chinese roads are foreign makes. One delegate involved in drawing up the recent eleventh five-year-plan for science and technology estimated that Chinese technology accounts for just 4 per cent of its exports of $140 billion a year.

Korea exemplifies the potential and the pitfalls of relying on national champions. The top ten Korean companies invest more than 4 per cent of sales in R&D. Companies such as Samsung Electronics have become household names around the world and models for a new kind of open, multinational Korea. Yet many critics believe most chaebol are stalling reforms to stifle new entrants, putting a brake on innovation.

Smaller companies account for 87 per cent of employment in Korea and 42 per cent of exports. Entrepreneurial companies are emerging in sectors being opened up by new technologies that are yet to be colonised by the chaebol. More than 600 biotech start-ups have been registered. A string of young Korean multimedia companies have gone international, such as the internet search company Naver. com, which has kept Google's Korean market share to 2 per cent. Chiasun Lim, an innovation specialist at Konkuk, suggests that Korean corporate innovation can be summed up in six words: 'Strong large firms, weak small firms'.

China
Chapter 2
P22

China's achievements in stem cell biology include the first clinical trials of adult stem cells as a treatment for traumatic brain injuries, led by neurosurgeon Jianhong Zhu at Fudan University. His patients, who have mostly suffered 'chopstick injury' as a result of arguments over a meal, are treated with neural stem cells extracted from their wounds, cultured and then reinserted.

India
Chapter 5
P32

Swati Piramal, director of Strategy and Communications for Nicholas Piramal Pharmaceuticals and the only woman on the Prime Minister's Scientific Advisory Council, is confident that: 'India will do things differently... At the beginning of my career all the talk was about reaching western standards, now it's about creating Indian standards.' Nicholas Piramal Pharmaceuticals' first global patent in 2001, for example, was for a product developed at a clinic in Canada, based on research initially in Mumbai and then in the UK, US, Taiwan and China... [Piramal's] goal is to get a new drug to market at a cost of $50 million, 1/20th of the cost of traditional approaches. 'It's a distant dream, but even if our estimates are out by 100 per cent that would still be a drug for only $100 million.' She claims they are on track to meet this target.

Korea
Chapter 6
P38

'Korea doesn't have to work with big pharma in the US or Europe; it can go straight to China where the view of health is totally different. We'll have our own system. The West will follow China as well and there will be huge effects.'

Jong Bhak, director, National Genome Information Center

## 7 New sciences in new ways

Hyang-Sook Yoo, until recently the director of one of Korea's most prestigious genetics programmes, spent three years researching her PhD on stomach cancer. The computerised machines in her lab at Daejeon can now do the same task in 30 minutes.

Yoo's lab exemplifies how abundant computer power is changing science, especially in emerging fields, such as bio and nanotech, which are more open to new entrants than already-mapped areas of scientific knowledge. Asia will not just produce more science but perhaps even new paradigms of science.

Dr Han Hoon, a Korean immunologist experimenting with stem cells in liver treatments, put it this way: 'We are in an era where the concept of medicine and treatment is changing to something other than the western drug approach. Cell therapy is a totally new field.' Asian science may blend eastern philosophies of prevention with the latest advances in genetics, and in the process leap ahead of western approaches.

Eras of science are defined by the tools that made them possible, from the telescope to logarithms and algebra. Today all sciences depend on computer power to handle large amounts of complex data. Top Asian research centres are investing in state of the art systems in buildings designed for the task. Jeffrey Wandsworth, director of the US Oak Ridge National Laboratory, told a conference in Seoul in March 2006: 'The barriers to doing excellent science in the bio/nano/info converged space are falling. Really only about a $300 million investment in infrastructure is needed. This is an area where any country could compete and the possibilities are wide open.'

Computer science will play a critical role in convergent sciences such as bioinformatics. The Indian government estimates its bioinformatics industry will be worth $2.5 billion by 2010. Meanwhile, China is pushing aggressively into nanoscience, which is expected to produce radical innovations in nerve and tissue repair, pollution control and surface coatings in the next 20 years. China ranks third in the world in nanoscience publications and ninth in terms of funding, with investment of $111 million in 2004. The Chinese Academy of Sciences is the fourth most cited nanoscience centre in the world after Berkeley, MIT and IBM.

Asia will also benefit from more rapid learning at the other end of the research pipeline, in testing and application. China may not yet lead the world in stem cell research but could do in applying research in clinical settings. India meanwhile opened the door to becoming the world's pharmaceutical guinea pig in 2006 by removing the constraint that drugs should be proven safe in their country of origin before being tested on Indians.

Asian countries will not just do more of the science we are familiar with. They will increasingly do new sciences in new ways as well.

China
Chapter 6
P47

In a recent interview with *Science*, Ouyang Zhingcan, director of CAS's Institute of Theoretical Physics, described an environment 'that's rife with simultaneous or serial duplicate manuscript submissions, self-plagiarized cookie-cutter papers, individual and institutional honorary authorship, and outright plagiarism'.

India
Chapter 6
P41

'All of us have some element of dual identity. We are global citizens in terms of ethics and governance. We want to follow the best global standards. But when we step outside the lab we become part of wider Indian society, which is more chaotic and occasionally corrupt. It's not straightforward.'

Dr LS Shashidara, Center for Cellular and Molecular Biology, Hyderabad

Korea
Chapter 3
P20

Hwan-suk Kim, who runs the Center for Democracy in Science and Technology (CDST), says that Hwang tapped into a potent mixture of insecurity and ambition in Korea: 'His style was very dangerous. Korea is still a very weak country and has a long way to go to become competitive, and he tapped into this insecurity.'

China
Chapter 6
P46

As Renzong Qiu observes, there is still a long way to go before China develops the more open, two-way forms of dialogue between science and society that are now commonplace in Europe: 'The scientists themselves have a vision, a sense of where their work might be taking us. But they don't open this up for discussion. Their views are expressed in closed rooms. When new programmes are developed, there's no debate involving the public – or even intellectuals. I think we urgently need a wider debate in Chinese society about where science is taking us, what it's for.'

## 8 Cultures and ethics of research

Jianhong Zhu, a neuroscientist at Shanghai's Fudan University, is pioneering the treatment of brain injuries using neural stem cells extracted from patients' wounds. Zhu is ahead of his field as Stephen Minger, director of the Stem Cell Biology Laboratory at the Wolfson Centre, King's College London, explained: 'If you discover something that you think is of clinical benefit, it's seen as unethical if you do not use it as soon as possible to treat patients.'

Will Asian science rise on the back of a more pragmatic, results-oriented, approach to ethics – an approach that many in Europe would find questionable?

Policy-makers in all three countries recognise that to do high-quality science they need to comply with the guidelines laid down by the international scientific community. Since 1998, for example, China has played an active role in international debates on stem cell research and genomics.

There is more doubt, however, over how regulations are enforced. According to Renzong Qiu, China's leading bioethicist, attempts to insert ethical issues into major science programmes are often put to one side on the grounds that 'the time is not yet right'. One researcher suggested that China's institutional review boards, which are meant to uphold ethical good practice, are 'like a rubber stamp. There are no suggestions, no revisions, no rejections.'

Weak public scrutiny, combined with pressure on scientists to deliver results, creates further ethical risks. One is the kind of fraud exposed in the case of the disgraced Korean stem cell researcher Woo-Suk Hwang. Jin Chen, a returnee lured back from the US with a research fund of £7.5 million, was fired as dean of microelectronics at Shanghai Jiatong University after passing off Motorola chips as his own. Plagiarism is rife in Chinese universities; New Threads, a Chinese language website based in the US, has exposed more than 500 cases of research fraud. In November 2006, the Chinese Ministry of Science and Technology responded to calls for tougher guidelines with a new office for 'research integrity'.

Another issue is human trials. India is positioning itself as a world centre for contract research through new legislation that means a drug developed abroad can be tested on Indians, without being first proved safe on humans elsewhere. Critics allege this is a charter for risky drugs to be tested on unwitting, poor and illiterate hospital patients. In Henan, China, HIV-positive villagers complained they had signed forms agreeing to be part of a drugs trial for a Californian firm without being told what the trials were for.

Asian scientists feel an allegiance to the global norms of science. However, in China and Korea science is also seen as a tool for economic development, and scientists feel powerful demands from state and corporate funders hungry for results. Even in democratic India, with its strong culture of NGO scrutiny, the accountability of science to civil society is weak. Asian science is in danger of developing in a democratic vacuum that may speed its growth but also distort it.

China
Chapter 4
P34

Contrary to the idea that 'the world is flat', the reality, as Richard Florida has argued, is remarkably spiky... In China, this phenomenon is acute. The three most innovative regions – the Yangtze River Delta (which includes Shanghai and 14 nearby cities), the Pearl River Delta (which includes Guangzhou, Shenzhen and Hong Kong) and the BoHai Rim (which includes Beijing and Tianjin) – account for just 3 per cent of China's land mass and 15 per cent of its population, but generate 45 per cent of GDP and over 70 per cent of international trade and investment. Just six cities – Beijing, Shanghai, Tianjin, Shenzhen, Shenyang and Guangzhou – produce 58 per cent of all invention patents.

India
Chapter 4
P26

'It used to be a question of three states, but all states are competing now... and so far we are only talking about the big cities... and just imagine if we brought other towns and cities into the mainstream.'

Dr Sridhar Mitta, CEO e4e Bengalooru

Korea
Chapter 4
P25

'London is international and people feel comfortable there. In the US, there is a sense that "our ethnicity is the world's ethnicity". By contrast, Korea, once dubbed the "hermit kingdom", is "very developed technologically, but also very provincial to international visitors".'

Tom Collins, Incheon Free Economic Zone

# 7 Next people, next places

Asia is not innovating: particular city regions in Asia are. Some well-known innovation centres – Bengalooru, which has 300,000 IT professionals among its population of seven million – are as intimately connected to global innovation networks as they are to their domestic economy.

Many more are waiting in the wings. We will have to learn a new geography of innovation that will include places like Pune and Hyderabad, Chongqing and Zhongguancun, Incheon and Daejeon.

All over Asia, regions aspire to be the next Silicon Valley. Yet few have Silicon Valley's ingredients for success: a dynamic interplay between universities and entrepreneurs, venture capitalist and large companies, knitted together by high-velocity labour markets and levels of skilled immigration. In India, poor infrastructure and low levels of indigenous start-ups are big obstacles. Korea's clusters tend to be dominated by government research institutes and large companies; there is less room for entrepreneurs and even less for immigrants. In China, knowledge parks mainly house high-tech manufacturing.

Instead of new Silicon Valleys, we are witnessing the growth of different kinds of innovation clusters in Asia.

By 2006 there were 53 knowledge parks in China with a further 30 planned by 2010. In the early 1990s, about 140,000 were employed in these parks; by 2006 it was 3.5 million.

In Korea, there are government-sponsored science cities, such as the Daedok Innopolis, with 53 research centres and more than 6000 PhDs; and Songdo, a new wireless city being planned in the free economic zone close to Incheon international airport. The Chinese equivalent is the Binhai New Area, a 90-mile strip on the north-eastern coast which will get US$15 billion of infrastructure investment in the next five years.

Then there are university-based clusters, such as the large Zhongguancun Science Park that has developed adjacent to Tsinghua University in Beijing. There are clusters associated with companies – such as the Pohang cluster in Korea linked to POSCO, the steel company – or the software cluster in Bengalooru with the outsourcers Wipro and Infosys at its heart.

Asia's urbanisation is also creating a set of world cities – Mumbai, Seoul, Shanghai, Beijing – which will sustain a mass of industry and science, culture and media. These cities could be future centres of innovation in global terms in the same way that Vienna, Paris, Manchester and Glasgow were in their day.

Congestion in Bengalooru is helping to promote alternative centres in Hyderabad and Pune. Korea's pervasive broadband infrastructure is creating new regional models for innovation. In China cities such as 31-million strong Chongqing aim to invest 2.5 per cent of local GDP in research and development by 2020, matching Shanghai's current investment levels. The next places for the next science are rising up fast.

India
Chapter 1
P07

'India is emerging as the swing state in the global balance of power.'

C Raja Mohan, 'India and the balance of power', *Foreign Affairs*, Jul/Aug 2006

Korea
Chapter 7
P43

'The desirable model is now joint R&D. Before 1997, everyone said "the Korean way is beautiful". After 1997, the Korea Development Institute said "collaboration is beautiful".'

Chaisung Lim, a science and technology studies professor at Konkuk University

China
Chapter 8
P58

As China continues its explosive growth, so does the market for speculation about its future. Some see China as an economic miracle that will run and run. Chris Patten, the former governor of Hong Kong, says he now has 'half a shelf of Sino-manic-books, which extrapolate gee-whiz statistics into a future noodle-eating paradise'. Others predict that internal contradictions will soon bring Chinese growth to a juddering halt: Will Hutton argues in a new book that China is 'reaching the limits of the sustainability of its current model, and to extrapolate from the past into the future as if nothing needs to change is a first-order mistake'. In the political realm, some see signs of an orderly move towards democracy, while others argue that any such transition is 'trapped'.

# 8 Prognosis

China, India and Korea are becoming more significant sources of innovation. Investments in innovation are rising and so are the outputs measured in scientific papers and patents. In key fields such as nanoscience in China and bioinformatics in India, that investment is being used productively to create world-class outcomes.

Yet predicting where things are headed next is tricky. The already significant differences between these countries' approaches to innovation may grow rather than diminish. Particular cities and regions will develop their own strengths.

Each country will produce innovations that reflect their particular mix of strengths and weaknesses. China's and Korea's development is based on products; India's growth relies on services. In China the state is at the centre of innovation efforts; in India the impetus comes from social networks and the private sector; and in Korea the chaebol have surpassed the state as the largest funders of R&D. China's innovation system is directed towards long-term goals. India's is diffuse and chaotic. China is not a democracy, India is. China wants independent innovation to lessen its reliance on the West. India is positioning itself as an interdependent innovator to connect with the West. China's innovation ideology is laced with techno-nationalism, India's with the cosmopolitan confidence of the global Indian elite. Compared with China, democracy may be India's strongest card, ensuring the freedom to think and debate, which may prove critical to long-term innovation.

Assessing where these countries' innovation systems are in 2006 is difficult enough. Casting forward to where they might be in ten or 15 years' time is fraught with uncertainty. In all three countries, the pursuit of innovation has triggered political and social tensions that will themselves shape how innovation develops.

China
Chapter 1
P09

On 17 October 2005, after a five-day voyage, the astronauts Fei Junlong and Nie Hasheng landed safely on the remote steppes of Inner Mongolia. This was China's second successful human space flight, after an initial mission in 2003. The government described it as a technological breakthrough, and announced it was planning its first space walk for 2007. 'Let us raise a welcoming toast to our heroes,' declared the Xinhua news agency. 'At this moment, history is returning dignity and sanctity to the Chinese nation.'

India
Chapter 8
P51

'The Indian influence across much of Asia has been one of culture, language, religion, ideas and values, not of bloody conquest. We have always been respected for our traditional export, knowledge! Does that not also make India a "global superpower", though not in the traditional sense! Can this not be the power we seek in the next century?'

Manmohan Singh, *Hindustan Times* India Leadership Summit, New Delhi, November 2006

Korea
Chapter 5
P32

'Chaebol have been and will be the dominant factor in Korea's industrialization and globalization.'

Kim, 1997

Korea
Chapter 7
P45

'Collaboration works best on an equal footing with younger people who have a different mindset. They are arrogant but in a positive way.'

Chris Ko at SAIT

### Nationalists vs cosmopolitans

Techno-nationalism places a priority on science for national economic development and uses science to project national power and status. If techno-nationalism gets the upper hand it will favour prestige projects in high-profile fields like defence and space. Cosmopolitan innovation starts from the reality that science increasingly depends on international collaboration, exchange and peer review. If cosmopolitan approaches gain the upper hand they will encourage regions to find specialist niches within linked global networks.

These tendencies are sibling rivals: inseparable but at odds. Techno-nationalists see innovation as a means to promote independence. Yet investing more in science-based innovation – as Korea found through the Hwang affair – requires greater openness to foreign ideas and international scrutiny.

The Seoul government is now trying to position Korea as a centre for cosmopolitan innovation, the R&D hub of north-east Asia. Yet much of Korean culture is still techno-nationalist; foreign investment into high-tech sectors is low because it is such a difficult place to do business.

China's policy promotes independent innovation and national champions, but the reality is that Chinese innovation is highly cosmopolitan; it depends heavily on returnees and foreign investment.

India is by far the most cosmopolitan, in part because by collaborating more closely with the US and others, it hopes to gain more strategic influence. In India, critics worry that too much interdependence has trapped Indian companies into servicing multinationals, rather than building up the indigenous knowledge base.

### Incumbents vs new entrants

Across Asia, governments are trying to shake up established research systems to make them more productive and market oriented. This is promoting a wave of new entrants into innovation, whether these are new institutions of science funding and research such as the ISER in India; returnees bringing ideas and methods from overseas; foreigners brought in to shake up the system like Robert Laughlin at KAIST; or entrepreneurial start-ups like Shanda in China.

At every turn, new entrants face a rearguard action from powerful incumbents who want investment in innovation without fundamental reform, whether these are chaebol in Korea or academics in China seeking to keep returnees at bay. In India many government labs remain resistant to reform.

Innovation in Asia will prosper the more room there is for new entrants and international approaches. The larger the share of increased spending on innovation that is captured by incumbents, the less impact it will have. Innovation will depend on how far reformers can go in challenging the status quo.

India
Chapter 6
P40

India's space programme is one of the best examples of Indian inventiveness: doing science on a grand scale, but in a way that also serves the needs of rural villages. And all on a tiny budget by international standards: annual funding for the space programme is only Rs 27 billion (US$600 million), 3 per cent of what NASA spends each year... In September 2004, ISRO launched Edusat, the world's first education satellite linking 5000 schools and colleges in five states. Plans have been drawn up to expand this into a nationwide space-based education service... Earth observation satellites have been used to combat deforestation, predict crop yields, trace water sources for irrigation and monitor desertification.

China
Chapter 3
P26

'Last year, it was the twentieth anniversary of my graduating class at Tsinghua, and they asked me to give a speech. I ended up saying, "Look, we all left in '85. When we left we were at the centre of China, we were in the mainstream of the mainstream. But now 20 years later, after so many of us have been abroad, who is in the mainstream? We need to start a movement of those who want to return to the mainstream." This idea created a real buzz. So we started a "mainstream forum", mostly for people from my year at Tsinghua, but also a few others. It's a place for people to share their experiences. It's for those who want to influence government and the institutions that exercise power in Chinese society.'

Li Gong, managing director, Windows Live China, Microsoft

India
Chapter 6
P39

India has over 1.5 million active NGOs.

### The elites vs the masses

In Korea, the elite route to innovation is to invest in superstar scientists to come up with breakthroughs in the mould of Dr Hwang. Korea's mass route will rely on ubiquitous innovation from a highly educated and connected population.

In India, the tensions between elite and mass innovation are even more potent. India is a democracy of mainly poor farmers. Yet innovation is mainly an activity of city-based elites. Elite innovation in India will always be vulnerable to a political backlash unless it can bring benefits to the 70 per cent of the population who live in India's 600,000 villages. There is much talk about innovation to create ultra low-cost products for poor consumers. The reality is that innovations that have improved living standards in rural India have tended to come from public funding, like the space programme or development NGOs.

China's lack of formal democracy does not make it immune from these tensions. Increased investment in innovation will directly benefit the city-based intellectuals, a key group the government needs to keep onside. But a national programme of innovation will succeed only if it also improves the basic living conditions for hundreds of millions of peasants who need clean water, energy, transport and food. A growing number of rural protests may force a change of direction towards more basic innovation.

### The state vs social networks

In China and Korea, the state plays a central role, orchestrating science and innovation as a tool for rapid economic development. Yet innovation thrives in an everyday democratic culture in which ideas can be openly aired, debated and tested. In China, this is still difficult, and successful innovation may depend on further economic and political reform.

In India the state's shortcomings put the onus on social networks to lead innovation, whether through the social networks of non-resident Indians and IIT alumni, or civil society networks of NGOs. Most of the action is outside the state.

Embracing science and innovation is in many ways the mark of a modern society: one that seeks to change itself through critical thinking. It is widely assumed that to do this a society must also take on the basic principles of liberal democracy: pluralism, tolerance, accountability and property rights. Yet China and India will be modern in quite different ways from one another and from the West. China is attempting an authoritarian modernisation combining markets and Communist rule. Indian innovation will be more open but also more fragmented, in a society of villages in which religion influences the way people think as much as science.

Indeed, competition between India and China may make them even less alike. China wants to assert itself against the US through techno-nationalism. India wants to gain influence with the US by being the swing state of Asia, open and cosmopolitan.

# 9  Where Britain stands

The graduate students gathered in a small room in a trendy café next to Tsinghua University had a very clear picture of Britain. The place that gave birth to Newton and Darwin, Watson and Crick, Rutherford and Tim Berners Lee was best known to them for Premiership football, castles, fog, island isolationism and Mr Bean.

An older group of former Chevening scholars who gathered one evening in Seoul were slightly kinder, but their overall impression was that Britain was a quirky place where it was possible to alight on teachers of great brilliance, but where unlike the US much of society was still inaccessible and closed.

India of course is different, tied to the UK by the postcolonial legacy of the English language, tea and cricket. Yet even in India there are unsettling signs. Asked whether the UK's special relationship with India was in danger of withering, Kapil Sibal, the science minister, told us: 'Yes, definitely.' Now Indians prefer to go to the US to learn and get rich.

Britain needs to ready itself for a world of global innovation networks, in which ideas and technologies will come from many more places. It needs to act now, while India and China's innovation capacity is still developing, and not in ten years' time when it is already too late.

Britain can ill afford to be vague about the kind of innovation it wants to be known for, not least because it will face huge strategic choices in a world in which there will be far more competition but also more opportunities for fruitful collaboration. Successful collaboration and competition both require more focus.

Science and innovation are where manufacturing and finance were 30 years ago: about to go global. Britain needs to learn lessons from those industries. The innovative part of the British car industry is now confined to a global niche making Formula One and Indy Cars after long, drawn-out efforts to rationalise the British mass-production car industry ran into the ground. Britain's science and innovation system might end up in just such a niche unless it embraces reform, raises its productivity and makes international collaboration central to its way of working.

The City of London could also have ended up as a cottage industry in world terms. But in the 1980s, its arcane practices were swept away and now the City is firmly established as one of the world's leading finance hubs. Britain's goal should be to develop the same 'City of London' model for science: cosmopolitan, skilled and efficient; open to new entrants and technologies; supported by trusted but business-friendly regulators.

Steering British science and innovation will mean facing some tough strategic choices, that go beyond simply levels of funding for R&D. Britain will not be able to compete with the scale and low cost of innovation resources in Asia. It will have to compete by using its resources more productively and creatively. That will require reforms to how science is funded, to promote innovation and research across disciplines; strengthening links across the innovation ecosystem between universities, business and finance; and ensuring that a culture of creativity and exploration thrives in universities.

Britain will need to make choices about which areas of science it wants to specialise in as other places build up their capabilities. It will need to rethink how it collaborates internationally and with whom: for example, by merging more British science programmes with partners in Europe or the US to gain economies of scale. How Britain governs and regulates science will be critical to this, securing public trust through greater and earlier openness to debate, while simultaneously supporting innovation in leading-edge fields such as stem cell research. Britain should lead the world in the good governance of innovation.

All of this needs to be wrapped up in a distinctive, national story of innovation for an economy that is largely based on services, culture, media and software. Too often, innovation policy has been designed to fight the last war, to revive Britain's vanishing manufacturing base, rather than to prepare for the next.

Our recommendations for how Britain should prepare for global innovation networks fall under five main headings:

| 1 | Unleash mass collaboration |
|---|---|
| 2 | Be a magnet for talent |
| 3 | Build the knowledge banks |
| 4 | Lead global science towards global goals |
| 5 | Get our story straight |

New analysis carried out by Evidence Ltd for this project as shown in the table below reveals that there has been a fourfold increase in China's collaborative authorship of research papers over the past ten years.

China
Chapter 7
P54

## Growth of research collaboration between China and other research-oriented economies

| Output | 1996 | 1999 | 2002 | 2005 |
|---|---|---|---|---|
| China – total papers | 15,218 | 23,174 | 33,867 | 59,543 |
| China – collaborative papers | 4489 | 7413 | 10,840 | 17,751 |
| US | 1364 | 2104 | 3267 | 5791 |
| European Union | 1320 | 2068 | 2881 | 4568 |
| UK | 430 | 646 | 895 | 1561 |
| Germany | 429 | 615 | 949 | 1381 |
| France | 213 | 294 | 441 | 827 |
| Canada | 294 | 402 | 566 | 1109 |
| Australia | 180 | 353 | 593 | 974 |
| Japan | 530 | 945 | 1461 | 2222 |
| Singapore | 75 | 204 | 359 | 726 |
| South Korea | 108 | 177 | 342 | 646 |

Source: Data from Thomson Scientific® and analysed by Evidence Ltd.

'Frankly speaking, the UK needs to invest more. The French offer joint funding, the Germans offer joint funding. But the UK doesn't. There's a lot of discussion about collaboration, but no actual money for projects.'

China
Chapter 7
P55

Richard Jiang, Shanghai Municipal Science and Technology Commission

'We've heard a lot about collaboration with the UK. But we want to know how to do it. Talking about it isn't enough. With the US, we know what we are doing, and there are links that go back many years as a result of all the scholarships and students who have spent time in the US.'

Professor Biliang Zhang, Guangzhou Institute of Biomedicine and Health

## 1 Unleash mass collaboration

Britain should become an evangelist for the globalisation of knowledge, by advocating and exemplifying cosmopolitan principles of open science and innovation. It should create a £100 million Global R&D Collaboration Fund, which the research councils could draw on in order to develop collaborative programmes with target countries on particular themes (eg clean energy in China, bioinformatics in Korea or climate science in India).

Bottom-up, scientist-led approaches still work well, and are producing large numbers of joint projects and co-authored papers. New research for this project by Evidence Ltd shows that Britain is the third most frequent collaborator with China, after the US and Japan.

But the bottom-up approach also breeds considerable frustration among collaborators, who criticise it for being too diffused. As one Indian scientist put it: 'We collaborate with the UK for friendship and with the US to do business.' The decentralised British approach does not fit well with top-down models of funding and decision-making in Korea and China. Nor can Britain afford to be complacent: France, Germany and the US, and new players like India and Brazil, are all upping their investment in collaboration.

New mechanisms are required that can combine the best of the British bottom-up model with additional elements of top-down investment and prioritisation. The £25 million UK–India Education and Research Initiative is a positive start. Similar schemes should now be developed for China and Korea.

Further steps could include:

— more targeted public–private joint ventures in emerging markets like environmental services, where it is possible to combine a British strength in research or technology with a local strength in application and development. The collaboration between the Hadley Centre at Reading University and the Indian Institute of Tropical Meteorology to predict the Indian monsoon is one model.

— larger companies helping smaller companies in their supply chain or sector to find new innovation partners abroad. More British universities need to follow the lead of Nottingham and Liverpool, which have pioneered joint ventures in Asia. Regional development agencies (RDAs) should be encouraged to pool more of their activities to avoid duplication, which often leaves potential partners confused.

— stronger leadership from the Office of Science and Innovation in orchestrating public funding from different sources – the research councils, government departments, the RDAs, the Technology Strategy Board, the National Endowment for Science Technology and the Arts – around key themes for collaboration. The UK needs the equivalent of a corporate 'R&D director', who can shape a more concerted strategy from the mass of bottom-up developments.

## Talent flows: Chinese, Indian and Korean student numbers in the UK

| | 1999/2000 | | | | 2004/2005 | | | |
|---|---|---|---|---|---|---|---|---|
| Country | Post-graduate | First degree | Other under-graduate | **Total** | Post-graduate | First degree | Other under-graduate | **Total** |
| China | 4190 | 1380 | 740 | **6310** | 28,170 | 20,820 | 3685 | **52,675** |
| India | 2620 | 940 | 210 | **3770** | 12,775 | 3105 | 805 | **16,685** |
| Korea | 1390 | 660 | 100 | **2150** | 1965 | 1525 | 360 | **3845** |

Source: Universities UK based on data from the Higher Education Statistics Authority.

China
Chapter 3
P30

Zhao Kuoying, a biology undergraduate at Tsinghua told us:

'In my department, there are 99 of us graduating this year. Seventy of these will go to the US. Twenty will stay at Tsinghua. Two will go to Sweden, two to France. And five don't yet know what they will do. I'm one of those.'

## 2 Be a magnet for talent

Like the City of London's success in financial markets, Britain's future as a centre for science and innovation rests on being open to attracting and retaining links with the best talent. Flows of scientists and entrepreneurs are the lifeblood of global innovation networks.

Britain does not do badly in terms of talent flows in comparison with most countries other than the US. As the table opposite shows, between 1999 and 2005 the number of students from China rose by 735 per cent, from India 343 per cent and from Korea 79 per cent. Britain is also home to large diaspora communities from India, China and Korea.

Yet while the numbers of Asian students is impressive, what the UK sometimes does with them is less so. Several of our interviewees in China and especially India complained of British universities treating foreign students as cash cows for mass-produced degree courses. Dispiriting experiences like this will quickly damage the reputation of UK higher education abroad.

To gain a better understanding of Britain's position in international talent flows, and the relationship between migration and innovation, the Economic and Social Research Council should establish a new research programme with the aim of creating a multidisciplinary body of knowledge and an annual talent flow report.

Scholarships and exchanges will remain critical as a way of strengthening collaborative networks. Currently, the Royal Society is developing plans for a new scholarship scheme. This should focus on postdoctoral and early to mid-career scientists, particularly those who have already had some engagement with British scientists and now want the opportunity for more sustained collaboration. The new scheme could be branded as the 'Darwin Fellowships' and launched in 2009 (to coincide with the 200th anniversary of Darwin's birth) with 200 places available each year.

At the same time, we need to send more UK scientific talent to Asia to support two-way flows of people and ideas. This will rely on improving general awareness of Chinese and Indian science and culture among students in the UK. We should encourage more schools to hire Chinese teachers and teaching assistants, and invest more in Asian studies at university. The decline in Asian studies and language learning in the UK is a worrying trend that must be reversed.

The UK should also aim to become the 'hosts with the most' – the convenor of the world's best scientific conferences, and the facilitator of interactive online spaces where scientists can meet. We should utilise social software and develop the science equivalent of MySpace or Facebook. The journal *Nature* is currently experimenting with this idea, which would build on the UK's position as a centre of science publishing.

University international strategies must now evolve from a commercial model, where maximising student numbers is the principal objective, to a collaborative model, where research links and joint projects take far greater priority.

### 3 Build the knowledge banks

A Chinese material scientist may next year produce a revolutionary type of nanomaterial. An Indian biochemist may come up with a blockbuster diabetes drug. Korean software engineers may develop the protocols for the next generation internet. More science is going to come from more people in more places. And the results will not necessarily be published in mainstream international journals.

Britain needs to invest more in understanding this new geography of science and innovation, and in gathering and distributing that information more effectively. We will be able to make sensible decisions about where and with whom to collaborate only through better mapping of bibliometrics, patents, student numbers and R&D investments.

Britain already benefits enormously from the work of the Foreign and Commonwealth Office's network of science and innovation advisers. This network now needs to be strengthened, with more posts and additional resources in China and India. Better mechanisms for sharing intelligence between the RDAs and universities would also help. Britain's highly decentralised approach to collaboration needs to be combined with improved coordination. In the same way that the Global Science and Innovation Forum (GSIF) enables the key science organisations in London to align their strategies, so 'mini-GSIFs' in priority countries could enable Britain to present a more united front to potential partners.

The proposed opening of Research Councils UK offices in China and India is a good idea, providing these are tightly linked to the work of the FCO. One of the tasks of those offices should be to monitor the number of collaborations that flow from bottom-up, response-mode funding. At the moment, there is little accurate data on this, and gathering it more systematically would enable Britain to better demonstrate the value of this model to the Chinese and Indian governments.

## 4 Lead global science towards global goals

Britain should stand up for science's contribution to an alternative narrative of globalisation: one that is not just about global markets and brands, but also about using global knowledge to address shared environmental and social challenges. The global innovation networks now being created by multinational companies need public counterparts: knowledge banks and research programmes that serve the global public interest.

Britain has at least one outstanding success in this field to build on: the international collaborative effort to unravel the genome of the worm, launched in Cambridge in 1956, which in turn helped to pave the way for the human genome project.

Britain should build on such successes and the ongoing work of the Wellcome Trust, which is one of the world's most innovative science foundations, to create the basis for a handful of 'global challenges' in science and innovation. Modelled on the 'X-Prize' for innovations in space flight or the Gates Foundation's support for key global challenges in healthcare, Britain should target funding to encourage its top researchers to collaborate with others across Asia, Europe and the US in pursuit of a small number of critical science-based challenges, for example in low-carbon energy, sustainable transport or disease prevention.

Britain should also lead the way in the creation of global knowledge and intellectual property banks, encouraging private sector companies to do the same. Another component of this could be the creation of a global, public and non-profit equivalent of the Innocentive science marketplace, in which more than 100,000 scientists offer to solve problems pitched at them by companies. Britain could sponsor the creation of a public equivalent aimed at the developing world.

Innovation is an inescapably public–private affair. In the past, national corporate research laboratories had their counterparts in public universities. As innovation goes global, so corporate innovation networks need a public counterweight. To take the lead as a cosmopolitan innovator, Britain needs to make these global public knowledge banks central to its strategy.

## 5  Get our story straight

Sitting in a plush hotel lobby in Beijing, Li Gong, head of Microsoft's Chinese internet business and an alumni of Cambridge University, put the challenge bluntly: 'China is the world's fastest-growing economy. The US is the home of Silicon Valley high-tech and Hollywood. What is the UK's one-line pitch to the world?'

In a world in which more ideas are coming from more sources, Britain can ill afford to be vague about what kind of innovation it wants to be known for. Ironically, as innovation policy has become central to developed economies, so it has become more imitative: everywhere nations and regions are trying to emulate Silicon Valley. Britain needs a more distinctive approach. We believe its story should include the following ingredients.

First, it must show how science-based innovation can strengthen an economy now largely based on services, software and culture. Second, it must promote excellence in science alongside more everyday forms of mass innovation. Third, it should promote Britain as a cosmopolitan centre, open to innovative talent from all over the world. Fourth, it must emphasise the importance of innovation for social and public goals, for example through promoting global knowledge banks.

Britain is no longer a society of mass industrial production. Instead it should aspire to be a society of mass innovation, mobilising know-how and creativity from many sources – not just scientists and engineers – and applying it to many fields – not just high-tech sectors.

China and Korea have created an education system that excels at rote learning. Britain should develop an education system for an innovation economy. An inflexible, standardised curriculum may be a good answer to the industrial economy's demand for punctual, literate, diligent workers capable of following the rules. An innovation economy requires an education system that is curiosity-led and promotes collaborative problem-solving.

Britain needs to make more of consumer-led innovation. Too often consumers are left out of innovation policy, but new leisure sectors like mountain biking were created almost entirely by avid consumer innovators. Consumers not technologists discovered the potential for SMS messaging.

Britain should also encourage a wave of citizen innovation because so many of the challenges we face are social. We must banish the nonsense that innovation comes only from the young. Older people are breaking new ground every day by finding ways to live healthily well into their 90s.

Innovative societies generally have a shared story that their citizens can relate to. Finland has an underdog story: a small nation surviving in the shadow of Russia thanks to its ability to adapt. In the Netherlands, innovation is focused on pragmatic collective adaptations – dams, dykes, bridges – which allow a society to live below sea level. In Korea, as we have seen, innovation is close to a national ideology, a self-conscious projection of dynamic change. In the US, innovation is about opening up frontiers for exploration and growth, from the railroads to the space race and into cyberspace.

Britain's dominant story about innovation, in contrast, is a lament for gifted boffins let down by inadequate systems of support. That will not do. We need to respond to Li Gong's challenge, and fast.

Britain needs an approach to innovation that is not just about the scientific elite, the trendy creative class or entrepreneurial superheroes but which recognises the contribution that everyone can make as consumers, citizens and creators. And this message must be cast in terms of cosmopolitan innovation: Britain as a place that is open to the world's best ideas, and which will support anyone from anywhere to put those ideas into practice.

'I do not believe that in the next stage of the global economy, success for one country need mean failure on the part of the other. Globalisation is not a zero sum game where one country or continent will only succeed at the expense of another.'

Gordon Brown MP, Chancellor of the Exchequer, speech at the Chinese Academy of Social Sciences, 21 February 2005

This pamphlet is one of a series of four published as the findings of the Atlas of Ideas project. For copies of the other reports, visit www.atlasofideas.org

We are very grateful to all our funders and to their representatives on the project steering group, including Lloyd Anderson, Mark Aspinall, Ben Brierley, Tony Bruce, David Dickson, Bob Driver, Tracey Elliot, Stephen Emmott, Neil Ferguson, Robert Fitter, Oliver Flude, Darren Gladwin, Chris Hale, Barbara Hammond, Rupert Harrison, Deborah Hordon, Ashley Ibbett, Neil Impiazzi, Bernie Jones, Tin Lin Lee, Catherine Marston, Tom McCarthy, Margaret McGarry, Elaine McMahon, Ewan Mearns, Ed Metcalfe, Stephen Minger, Frans Nauta, Mark Palmer, Graham Paterson, Tony Peatfield, Mark Pitman, Carol Rennie, Keith Sequeira, Ken Snowden, Bert van den Bos, Joeri van den Steenhoven, Michael Walker, Mark Wathen, Michael White and James Withers.

Our fieldwork would not have been possible without the advice and practical support that we received from the Foreign and Commonwealth Office's science and innovation network in China, India and Korea. We are also grateful to the embassies of each country in the UK. Above all, we are indebted to the almost 400 policy-makers, scientists, R&D managers and other experts whom we interviewed over the course of the project.

Finally, at Demos, thanks to Kirsten Bound, Molly Webb, Paul Miller and Anna Maybank for the enormous collective effort that has gone into the Atlas project over the past 18 months; to Julie Pickard for her skilful copy-editing; and to Tom Bentley, Grahame Broadbelt and Catherine Fieschi for guidance when it was most needed. Any errors and omissions in this report remain our own. The views expressed are those of the authors and do not necessarily reflect those of our project funders.

**Charles Leadbeater** and **James Wilsdon**
January 2007